Miracle Malcolm

Written By:

Ariel Simmons

For information address Ariel Simmons via email at bookings.arielsimmons@gmail.com.

Library of Congress Control Number:2019913288

ISBN 978-0578572819

Dedication:

To my Miracle baby; thank you for inspiring me to a whole new level
and for giving life a whole new meaning.
Mommy loves you beyond the imaginable.

About this Book:

Preterm birth is defined as a baby being born prior to 37 weeks. According to March of Dimes, in the U.S. approximately 1 in 10 babies are born prematurely. That's an estimated 15 million babies a year that are born too early.

Premature awareness month is in November

MIRACLE MALCOLM

Hi, my name is Malcolm!

I have ten toes, two eyes, and a nose just like you
-but I am also a miracle.

You might be wondering
what a miracle might be, it's
when amazing things happen it's true!

I am Miracle Malcolm and let me tell you why.

It all began October 30th. I just could not wait
any longer in Mommy's belly.

I could hear her laughing; I could hear dad laughing too,
and I was tired of missing the fun.

So I came out as soon as I could,
but apparently, I was too early.

I was only ONE pound, which is much too small.

But don't worry because I'm Miracle Malcolm.

My ten toes were too small, and so were my lungs.

I couldn't go home just yet you see; there were doctors around me,
nurses, and warm blankets, but most importantly my Mom and Dad.

I think I was too impatient because instead of Mommy's tummy,
I was now stuck in a little warm box with tubes.
No matter how scary it was, my Mom and Dad were there.

But don't worry because I'm Miracle Malcolm.

PG 6

Day after day my little toes grew,
my eyes, my hair, and my smile. I started to
hear better, I started to see better,
I started to feel better too.
I was growing day by day!

That was why I had to stay,
to get better and stronger.

Plus, Mom and Dad were always there.
They came to see me for 3 whole months!
They must love me a lot.

Because I am Miracle Malcolm.

I had so many baby neighbors -
ones who also just couldn't wait like me.

We chatted about how small we were and
dreamt about being in our own beds.

I didn't know when I would get to go home but I
tried my best each day.

Because I am Miracle Malcolm.

The doctors worked very hard
and the nurses would check on us too.

I never felt lonely or scared because
there was always someone there.
The doctors looked so worried when I first arrived,
but they were now smiling again.

Probably because I am Miracle Malcolm

"It's time to go home." I heard the doctor
say and packed my bags
as quick as could be!

My parents carried me out like I was a Prince!
They gave me hugs and kisses and I got to
smell outside for the first time.

As soon as we arrived back at our home castle,
I knew I was going to like it there.

It was perfect for Miracle Malcolm.

PG13

Although I got to go home, I was still smaller
than other babies. They were big enough
to crawl and play.

Sometimes it was still hard for my little hands,
but I was still smiling no matter what.
My dad would wrap me up tight and had
funny jokes and my mom would
play with my hair and give great kisses and hugs.

No matter how small or different I might be, I knew I was loved.

Because I am Miracle Malcolm.

So, who knows how big I might grow,
or small I might stay.

I will always be kind to my baby friends because
we each have a story to tell.

Some might look different, some might talk different,
but that doesn't matter to me.

You'll always see a smile on Miracle Malcolm's face.

We all have our own miracle.

We all need to smile, hug,
kiss, and care for each other, you know.
My baby journey started out wild, so many things
happened at once all so fast!

If that was how I came into the world,
who knows what adventure might happen next!

I'm full of surprises!

Because I am Miracle Malcolm, and I'm here to stay.

PG18

About the Author

Born and raised in the Chicagoland area, Ariel Simmons found her gift at an early age.
The moment her pen touched paper she was forever bound to her love, writing. Like most, she found fulfillment in other activities but nothing could compare to her first love. At the age of 10 she began writing books of poetry transitioning to screenplays in high school. Thereafter, her writing slowed down but by the grace of God she was reacquainted with her first love through the birth of her son Malcolm.

In her debut children's book Miracle Malcolm, she showcases her talents to
the world as an author in hopes of inspiring, educating and spreading
positivity to those around her.

Ms. Simmons currently resides in Bolingbrook, IL.

CPSIA information can be obtained at www.ICGtesting.com
Printed in the USA
LVIW012141171119
637645LV00012B/250

9 780578 572819